GREAT BIBLE STORIES

KING SOLOMON

Adapted by Maxine Nodel　　**Illustrated by Norman Nodel**

BARONET BOOKS is a registered trademark of Playmore Inc., Publishers
and Waldman Publishing Corp., New York, N.Y.

BARONET BOOKS, NEW YORK, NEW YORK
Printed in China

King David taught his young son
Solomon always to walk in the ways
of the Lord.

When Solomon was a very young man,
he became king of Israel.

But Solomon was afraid he didn't
know how to rule well over his people.

So, of all the gifts that God could give him,
Solomon asked only for wisdom.

Solomon's asking for wisdom pleased God, and he made the young king rich and powerful as well.

Solomon ruled with justice and fairness, and the people of Israel trusted him and relied on his judgment.

Word of Solomon's wealth and wisdom spread all over the world. People came from everywhere to see him and seek his advice.

One day, two women came rushing into the court.
One carried a baby.

The women stood before King Solomon. Each claimed the baby was hers.

There were no witnesses who knew the truth. The entire court was puzzled. At last, Solomon ordered, "Bring me a sword."

"Cut the baby in half," said Solomon. "Then each of them can have part of him."

One woman agreed. But the other fell to her knees, crying. "Don't kill my baby," she pleaded. "Better that she may have him and he lives."

"That is the true mother," said Solomon.
"Give her the child!"

Soon, Solomon began his greatest task, building God's temple in Jerusalem.

The finest materials and the greatest craftsmen in the world were brought to the temple.

It took seven years to complete the work
of the temple. Many of its walls were covered in gold.

Great pillars and statues supported and adorned
the magnificent building.

Now all the people could come to worship God in his holy tabernacle.

Building the temple made Solomon even more famous and respected.

In a faraway land, another monarch was curious about the great king of Israel. She was the Queen of Sheba.

With all of her court and followers, she journeyed to meet Solomon in Jerusalem.

The queen didn't believe all she had heard about this king.
She wanted to see, and hear, for herself.

Solomon welcomed the beautiful queen and thanked her for her fine gifts.

The queen listened carefully as Solomon made his judgments. She marvelled at the magnificence of his temple.

"You are the wisest man and greatest king in the world, Solomon!" she declared.

Then she returned to her land with the riches the king gave her.

Solomon ruled Israel for forty years.
He left a country rich, strong, and at peace.